THE

VAMPIRE
HUNTER'S

HANDBOOK

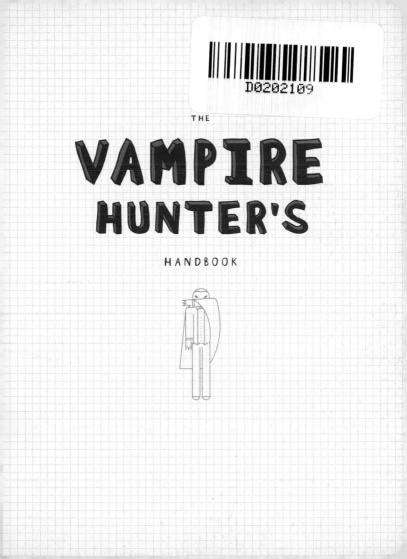

THE

VAMPIRE

HUNTER'S

HANDBOOK

by Erin Slonaker

PENGUIN BOOKS

PENGUIN BOOKS

Published by the Penguin Group
Penguin Books Ltd, 27 Wrights Lane,
  London W8 5TZ, England
Penguin Putnam Inc., 375 Hudson Street,
  New York, New York 10014, USA
Penguin Books Australia Ltd, Ringwood,
  Victoria, Australia
Penguin Books Canada Ltd, 10 Alcorn Avenue,
  Toronto, Ontario, Canada M4V 3B2
Penguin Books India (P) Ltd, 11 Community
  Centre, Panchsheel Park, New Delhi -
  110 017, India
Penguin Books (NZ) Ltd, Cnr Rosedale
  and Airborne Roads, Albany, Auckland,
  New Zealand
Penguin Books (South Africa) (Pty) Ltd,
  5 Watkins Street, Denver Ext 4,
  Johannesburg 2094, South Africa

On the World Wide Web at: www.penguin.com

Penguin Books Ltd, Registered Offices:
Harmondsworth, Middlesex, England

First published 2001
1

Designed and Illustrated by Paul Kepple
and Timothy Crawford @ Headcase Design,
Philadelphia, Pennsylvania

Made and printed in England by Clays Ltd,
St Ives plc

British Library Cataloguing in Publication Data
A CIP catalogue record for this book is
available from the British Library

ISBN 0-141-31418-4

PHOTOGRAPHY CREDITS

pg. ii: Bettmann/CORBIS

pgs. vi–vii: Janet Wishnetsky/CORBIS

pg. ix: Janet Wishnetsky/CORBIS;
(bat) © VCG/FPG

pg. x: (full bleed) Kobal Collection;
(insets, clockwise from top)
Michael & Patricia Fogden/CORBIS,
Jeff Vanuga/CORBIS, Dallas & John
Heaton/CORBIS, Danny Lehman/CORBIS

pg. 4: (left) Peter Wilson/CORBIS; (right) Janet
Wishnetsky/CORBIS

pg. 8: (bottom) Richard T. Nowitz/CORBIS;
(left inset) © 1995 Jeffrey Luther/PC Design.
All rights reserved. www.pulpcards.com;
(right inset) Bettmann/CORBIS

pg. 11: Warner/MPTV

pg. 18: Bettmann/CORBIS

pgs. 36–37: Bettmann/CORBIS

pg. 42: VCG/FPG

pgs. 50–51: Universa/MPTV

pg. 52: Janet Wishnetsky/CORBIS

pg. 53: Nik Wheeler/CORBIS

pg. 54: (top) Robert Holmes/CORBIS;
(bottom) Danny Lehman/CORBIS

pg. 55: Robert Holmes/CORBIS

pg. 61: Everett Collection

pg. 62: Kobal Collection/Hammer

pgs. 66–67: MGM/MPTV

pg. 78: Everett Collection

CONTENTS

INTRODUCTION

Do you have what it takes to be a Vampire Hunter? Do you have the strength, cunning and wit to battle these legendary creatures of the night? Have you ever wondered whether the stories of the 'undead' creatures that feed on human blood were real or just old wives' tales?

You may have heard that vampires are a thing of the past or you may believe they live among us today. Either way, if you're curious enough to wonder, then you may just have the makings of a successful Vampire Hunter.

TV programmes and films may make vampire hunting look simple, but a true vampire specialist understands that the only way to do battle with a vampire – in fact or fiction – is to know the opponent.

That's where this book comes in. Because vampires may take many forms, you have to know the basic characteristics to look for. *The Vampire Hunter's Handbook* has been created to teach the tell-tale signs that identify a vampire beyond the shadow of a doubt. Armed with this knowledge, a Vampire Hunter will be able to mount his or her best defence.

This book will teach you how to find vampires and how to protect yourself against them. You'll also get some good advice for avoiding or even conquering them (if it comes down to that, which hopefully it won't). If you're ready and willing, then read on, and learn all the tricks of the vampire hunting trade.

CHAPTER ONE

WHAT IS A VAMPIRE?

Stories about vampires have been around for ages. The earliest vampires are believed to have first appeared in a small Romanian village in the 1300s. When people and animals mysteriously died during the night, the villagers explained these strange deaths by placing the blame on a spirit (never an actual person – or even a disease). The word for this spirit, *vampir*, whose original meaning is unknown, later became *vampire* in French.

It's the name that English speakers heard and added to their own language.

But other versions of the vampire existed long before even the 1300s. In ancient Greece, for example, the *lamiae* (lahm-ee-i) were thought to suck the blood of young children. And in seventeenth-century China, the bloodthirsty *jiang-shi* (jiang-shur), which means 'corpse', or 'dead body', returned from the dead to kill villagers and animals.

Perhaps the most famous vampire of all time, however, was the real-life Transylvanian count known as Dracula. There have been books – such as Bram Stoker's 1897 novel *Dracula* – and films – like the 1931 version starring the old-time actor Bela Lugosi – about Vlad Dracula. But not everyone realizes that this larger-than-life character was a living person – at least at one time.

VLAD DRACULA
(A.K.A. VLAD THE IMPALER)

Born in the early 1400s, Vlad Dracula (dra-kool-a) was the son of Vlad Dracul (dra-kool), the ruler of Wallachia. They lived very close to Transylvania, a region of northern Romania nestled in the Carpathian Mountains. The older Vlad had taken the name Dracul, which is Romanian for 'devil' or 'dragon'. As the 'son of Dracul', the younger Vlad was known as 'Vlad Dracula'.

Vlad Dracula ascended the throne after his father was killed in a battle against the Turkish army. Angry about his father's death, Dracula ruled his kingdom with a bloody hand, engaging his territory in many wars with the Turks. Even though he was in power for only six years, Dracula was responsible for the deaths of thousands. He loved mass murders, and the ground around his castle was always red with blood.

Dracula was murdered by an assassin in 1476, but his legend lived on well past his death. Mysterious deaths, bumps in the night and other inexplicable events in Transylvania were all blamed on his spirit. Over time, the people of Transylvania devised a complete story about his 'life' after death, in which his spirit sought out the blood of the living.

Bram Stoker was inspired by these stories and wrote the novel *Dracula* in 1897. Stoker's Count Dracula embodied nearly all the characteristics of vampires for years to come. (You'll learn about all of these typical characteristics later.)

ELIZABETH BATHORY

Elizabeth Bathory was a Hungarian countess in the late 1500s. According to several accounts, Bathory would murder her servants and then bathe in blood that was drained from their bodies. Apparently, she was obsessed with blood – she loved the sight, feel and smell of it, and felt that it made her physically stronger. For good reason, people called her the 'Blood Countess'.

Bathory was tried for crimes against her servants and sentenced to life in prison. She was locked in a room in her castle with no windows and only small slits for air. Amazingly, she was able to survive in this prison for three years.

After she died, any mysterious deaths in the town were blamed on her spirit. According to legend, she returned from the grave as a vampire and continued her quest for blood.

PETER PLOGOJOWITZ

In September of 1728, a simple farmer from Hungary named Peter Plogojowitz died at age 62. Three days later, however, he calmly walked into the kitchen of his home and asked his son to get him some food. His son was confused but gave him a bowl of soup. Peter ate the food, left the house and returned two nights later, asking to be fed again.

This time his son refused to give him anything to eat – which turned out to be a bad idea. The son was found dead the next morning, but his body appeared unharmed. Soon after the son was found, other villagers became weak and sick. Doctors said that the people were suffering from an excessive loss of blood. The victims said that in their dreams, Peter had come to them and had bitten them on the neck. Within a week, nine of the sick villagers had died.

In an attempt to solve the mystery, all the graves of the recently dead were dug up. The condition of Peter's body surprised everyone: his skin was plump, his eyes were open and there was fresh blood on his mouth.

The people of the town knew right away that he was a vampire, so they called in an executioner. The executioner drove a stake through the body and then the villagers burned the body. None of the other corpses seemed to be vampires, but they reburied the bodies with lots of garlic just in case. Their efforts were successful — Peter never came back to torment the village again.

LESTAT DE LIONCOURT

Lestat de Lioncourt is a fictional character created by the modern writer Anne Rice — but stories indicate that he may have been inspired by a real vampire. No Vampire Hall of Fame would be complete without him.

Lestat is featured in Rice's series of novels called *The Vampire Chronicles*, where readers learn the many details of his long life. A vampire for nearly two centuries, Lestat lived and killed all over the world, from Paris to London to New Orleans. (Once you're doomed to live for ever, you get the urge to see new places.)

DRACULA: A BRIEF SUMMARY

In the novel *Dracula* by Bram Stoker, an unsuspecting Englishman named Jonathan Harker travels to Transylvania to finalize a property deal in London with Count Dracula. But while Harker is in Transylvania, the Count is off feeding on the blood of two women back in London—one of whom is Harker's fiancée, Mina.

Once Harker learns that Dracula is a vampire, he seeks to destroy him with the help of several friends, including Abraham Van Helsing. They place crosses in Dracula's coffins and then invade Castle Dracula. They manage to kill Dracula by beheading him and putting a stake through his heart. This appears to be the end of Count Dracula—but certainly not the end of the vampire legend.

DEAD OR ALIVE?

All vampires have one thing in common: they refuse to stay dead.

Vampires, in fact, belong to the world of the 'undead', a strange kind of existence that leaves them neither living nor dead. More than anything, vampires want to defeat death. And the only way they can do this is by constantly feeding on the blood of the living. This blood has a life-force that is crucial to all vampires' survival; without it, their bodies would continue to rot and decay just like a regular corpse.

In order to maintain a constant blood supply, vampires find victims, bite them (typically on the neck, where the jugular vein provides a steady stream of blood) and drain just enough blood to satisfy their need – but often not enough to actually kill their victims. After all, once a vampire finds a host human to feed on, it can revisit its victim again and again for many nights to come, so long as the human doesn't die—or catch on to the vampire's habit. (If you suspect that you're being visited by a vampire, just take the quiz on pages 12–13.)

The results of a vampire bite are more than a simple pain in the neck. Losing blood can be very dangerous, leaving the human woozy and disoriented. But even more dangerous is the fact that, once bitten, a vampire victim runs the risk that he or she may *become* a vampire (you'll learn why in the next section).

VAMPIRE

CONVERTED VICTIM

1 VAMPIRE   2 HUMAN VICTIM   3 NECK, TYPICAL PLACE OF BITE

ARE YOU OR IS SOMEONE YOU KNOW A VAMPIRE?

Have you ever suspected a friend or neighbour of being a vampire? What if you are a vampire and don't even know it? Take this quiz for yourself and apply the questions to anyone you're suspicious of to find out if your hunches are correct.

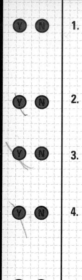

1. Do you have two strange marks on your neck, wrists or ankles, spaced about an inch and a half apart?

2. Would you rather stay inside sleeping all day than go to school?

3. Do you find it easy to read a book in the dark because your eyesight is so good?

4. Does looking at the sun cause you extreme physical pain? Do you burn very easily in the sun?

5. When you look into the mirror, do you have no reflection?

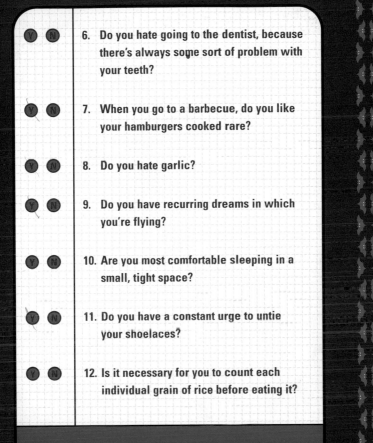

Y N	6.	Do you hate going to the dentist, because there's always some sort of problem with your teeth?
Y N	7.	When you go to a barbecue, do you like your hamburgers cooked rare?
Y N	8.	Do you hate garlic?
Y N	9.	Do you have recurring dreams in which you're flying?
Y N	10.	Are you most comfortable sleeping in a small, tight space?
Y N	11.	Do you have a constant urge to untie your shoelaces?
Y N	12.	Is it necessary for you to count each individual grain of rice before eating it?

If you answered 'yes' to four or more questions, take caution: There is a strong chance you or someone you know is a vampire.

HOW VAMPIRES ARE MADE: VAMPIRES IN WAITING

Once a vampire has chosen someone as its host, it can decide to turn that person into a vampire. There isn't a special ceremony—a new vampire doesn't get a framed certificate or an ID card. All a vampire has to do is drain the blood until the host dies, and then bite him once more after death.

Sometimes a vampire changes people into vampires just for the fun of it, to watch the town or city try to fight a sudden vampire infestation. At other times, it just wants some company. It's really up to the individual vampire to decide whether its victim will also become a vampire.

According to legend, vampires can be created in at least three other ways as well.

① If an animal leaps over an open grave as the coffin is being lowered into it, the body in the coffin could return as a vampire.

ANIMAL LEAPING OVER
OPEN GRAVE

① WORRIED MOURNER | ② OPEN GRAVE | ③ LEAPING ANIMAL

② If a ray of moonlight falls on to a dead body or coffin as it is buried, or if the corpse is somehow reflected in the light of a mirror during burial, the body could return as a vampire.

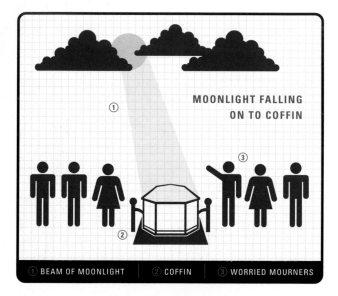

MOONLIGHT FALLING ON TO COFFIN

① BEAM OF MOONLIGHT · ② COFFIN · ③ WORRIED MOURNERS

(3) Finally, there are some unfortunate humans who are simply destined to become vampires, and nothing can change their fate. A vampire is often the seventh son born to a seventh son. Clues to their identities are easy to spot: as babies they may be born with a full set of teeth and lots of hair, and throughout their lives they'll show a lot of interest in cemeteries and blood, and they'll generally be 'night' people.

SEVENTH SON OF A SEVENTH SON

① ② ③ ④ ⑤ ⑥ ⑦

①—⑥ FIRST SIX SONS | ⑦ SEVENTH SON WITH TEETH AND HAIR

CHAPTER TWO

VAMPIRE BEHAVIOUR

When most people die, their bodies are placed in coffins designed to be eternal resting places, and that's that. Vampires, on the other hand, aren't content to sleep forever and are constantly getting up to roam around. But a vampire's coffin and the soil of the town where it's buried do have meaning for the vampire, and they're the best places to start looking for one.

In fact, the vampire must be in close proximity to its coffin and native soil in order to survive. If separated from either for very long, the vampire will become very weak. As a result, most vampires return to their coffins during the day to sleep and 'recharge' their energy.

Generally, a young vampire must live in its coffin for at least seven years before it can relocate to a new area. After seven years, some vampires will move to new cities, just for a change of pace.

According to some reports, Dracula always travelled with a coffin full of soil from his native Transylvania, so that he could leave home for months at a time. Although the soil does not have to be inside the coffin, most vampires find this the safest and most convenient way to be sure they have access to it at all times. By sleeping *in* this dirt, they can feel at home.

WHEN VAMPIRES ARE ACTIVE: CREATURES OF THE NIGHT

We know that the sun's UVA and UVB rays can be harmful – who isn't always being reminded to put on more sunscreen? But a nasty sunburn is nothing compared to what a vampire experiences outdoors on a sunny day. Sunlight can actually set a vampire on fire! Some vampires will turn to dust if even the smallest ray of sunlight hits them, so they do not go outside at all during the day (unless it's very cloudy and overcast).

Other vampires are simply weakened by the light and lose their energy to hunt during daylight hours. To be safe, vampires avoid being active while the sun is out.

WHAT VAMPIRES LOOK LIKE: VAMPIRES AMONG US

Whichever way it became a vampire, there are some basic clues to identify these creatures of the night. Remember, vampires often look just like ordinary human beings. (After all, until recently, they *were* ordinary human beings.) A Vampire Hunter must be observant to work out just who is friend and who is foe.

PHYSICAL CLUES

Glowing eyes: Many have observed that a vampire's eyes seem to glow – kind of like a cat's eyes. (Some experts say a vampire's eyes glow red, while others think they are more yellow or green.) These eyes can have a hypnotic effect on people; some victims may feel an uncontrollable need to look into a vampire's eyes, even if they are disgusted by the creature's appearance. This is how many vampires trick their prey; by keeping their victims from running away, vampires can get close enough to bite them.

Sharp fangs: Like their cousins the werewolves (people who transform into wolves under full moons), vampires have long canine fangs that allow them easily to penetrate a victim's skin.

Because their fangs are so noticeable, vampires keep their mouths closed when smiling – after all, most of us would notice if a person had unusually long and sharp canine teeth. Vampires want to avoid suspicion at all costs, even if it's a struggle to keep from laughing aloud at a good joke!

Also, their sharp teeth often cause vampires to bite their lips accidentally. Small wounds near the lips are another common indication that someone is a vampire.

Animal features: Also like werewolves, vampires may

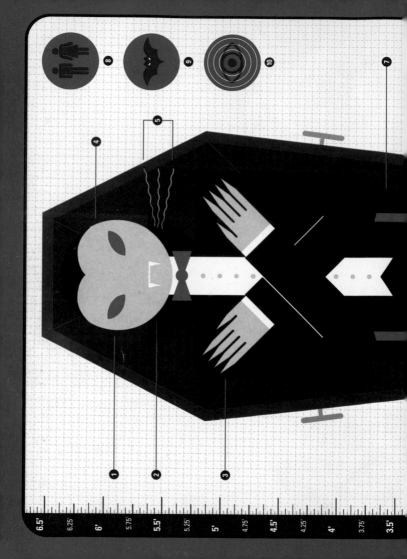

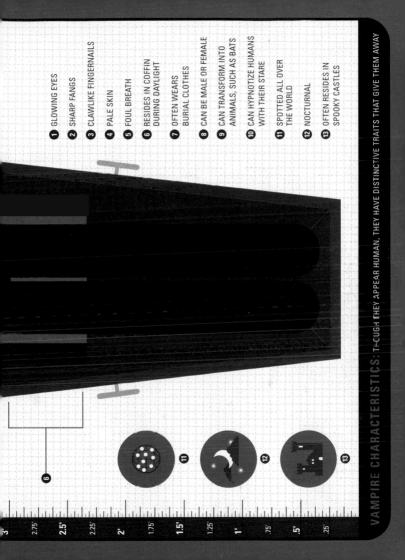

1. GLOWING EYES
2. SHARP FANGS
3. CLAWLIKE FINGERNAILS
4. PALE SKIN
5. FOUL BREATH
6. RESIDES IN COFFIN DURING DAYLIGHT
7. OFTEN WEARS BURIAL CLOTHES
8. CAN BE MALE OR FEMALE
9. CAN TRANSFORM INTO ANIMALS, SUCH AS BATS
10. CAN HYPNOTIZE HUMANS WITH THEIR STARE
11. SPOTTED ALL OVER THE WORLD
12. NOCTURNAL
13. OFTEN RESIDES IN SPOOKY CASTLES

VAMPIRE CHARACTERISTICS: THOUGH THEY APPEAR HUMAN, THEY HAVE DISTINCTIVE TRAITS THAT GIVE THEM AWAY

develop long, pointed, claw-like fingernails. Most smart vampires keep these carefully trimmed so they don't raise any suspicions.

Pale skin: Most people lose their summer suntans during the winter months – but they'll *never* be as pale as a vampire! Vampires are more pale than living people and their skin is cold to the touch. Even though vampires are no longer truly 'living', their skin never rots. If it's been a while since they've fed, vampires may look especially ill, but once they've located a blood supply, they become warmer, and their skin and lips get rosier.

Foul breath: Prominent teeth aren't the only reason vampires are selective about opening their mouths. A vampire's breath smells like rot and decay, since their internal organs aren't in very good condition. (They're essentially dead, after all.)

A DESCRIPTION OF DRACULA
ACCORDING TO BRAM STOKER'S *DRACULA*

(Have a dictionary handy!)

His face was a strong—a very strong—aquiline, with high bridge of the thin nose and peculiarly arched nostrils; with lofty domed forehead, and hair growing scantily round the temples but profusely elsewhere. His eyebrows were very massive, almost meeting over the nose, and with bushy hair that seemed to curl in its own profusion. The mouth, so far as I could see it under the heavy moustache, was fixed and rather cruel-looking, with peculiarly sharp white teeth; these protruded over the lips, whose remarkable ruddiness showed astonishing vitality in a man of his years. For the rest, his ears were pale, and at the tops extremely pointed; the chin was broad and strong, and the cheeks firm though thin. The general effect was one of extraordinary pallor.

As a result, vampires are very particular about dental hygiene, and they brush their teeth more than non-vampires. Keep an eye (and nose) out for someone whose breath smells really bad – or whose breath is always minty-fresh.

BEHAVIOUR CLUES

Vampires also have a lot of supernatural powers they can use to confuse even the best Vampire Hunter.

Controlling the weather: One of the most amazing powers a vampire possesses is the ability to control the weather. As stated earlier, vampires cannot stand to be in sunlight. Even a small amount of exposure to sunlight will reduce their strength, and under some circumstances actually destroy them.

So it's definitely to their advantage to be able to churn up a fog or a storm quickly – without sunlight, there's nothing to keep them indoors.

Be extra careful of areas where there's been fog for several days in a row, and watch out for sudden fog or storms. There could be a vampire in the midst of the mist!

Lack of reflection: Despite looking just like normal people, vampires reportedly, against all the laws of physics, do not reflect light the same way ordinary people do. This means their images will not show up in mirrors or be reflected in water, and they will not show up in photos of any kind! (Even a digital camera won't catch them!)

Also, many people become suspicious when they see someone with 'red eye' in a photograph. This is not a glimpse of their true vampire natures, however – it's just bad photography. Remember: A vampire will not show up on film *at all*.

Superhuman strength: Vampires have superhuman strength and can use it to escape dangerous situations; for

example, they could easily break down a door. It's important to be prepared for this, and you should plan to match their physical strength with your own brainpower. (You'll learn some clever ways to outwit vampires in the next section.)

Infrequent breathing: Keep an eye out for irregular or abnormal breathing in people you suspect are vampires. (This is worse than someone with a stuffy nose, so don't be confused.) Vampires breathe very rarely – if at all – because they don't need air to survive.

Vampires can make themselves breathe in order to escape a sharp-eyed observer's detection. But while it's difficult for a vampire to sustain this during the day, it's impossible while they sleep; a slumbering vampire will not breathe at all.

WARNING: Because they don't need air, vampires can easily hide under water for long periods of time. It's not a good idea to chase a vampire by swimming after it, because the vampire can stay under water much longer than a living, breathing human being.

No need for food: Vampires have no use for traditional food because they get all their nutrients from human blood. They will eat normal food if they want to blend in with normal humans, but they don't require it for survival. Be suspicious of people who don't eat much.

Shape-shifting: Some vampires – but not all – can 'shape-shift', which means they can turn themselves into animals (they 'shift' into another 'shape'). Unlike werewolves (who turn into wolves once a month), a vampire can change into *any* animal – a bat, a butterfly, a rat, anything – whenever it wants to. It cannot remain in animal form for more than a few hours, however, and will use its shape-shifting powers only for short trips or quick escapes.

Skilled Vampire Hunters will pay close attention to the animals in their neighbourhoods. It is not uncommon to see a dog that looks 'kind of human', or a cat that appears to understand human speech. And, in many instances, there may be a supernatural explanation for these strange animals.

Defying gravity: Some vampires can fly or at least float many feet into the air. A vampire with the power of flight is a dangerous enemy. If a person comes face to face with one, the vampire may suddenly take off and fly away – or even fly at the person. Because of this risk, most experts assume that all vampires they encounter can fly, until they learn otherwise.

HOW TO KEEP VAMPIRES AWAY: TRADITIONAL VAMPIRE REPELLENTS

The last few pages have discussed all of the powers that vampires have. Now for the good news: Vampire Hunters have plenty of powers too. The following is a list of all the repellents that are painful, deadly or just plain uncomfortable for a vampire.

Garlic: Vampires from around the globe just hate this pungent plant. A vampire will do whatever it can to avoid garlic, especially if it's raw. Cooked garlic doesn't have quite the same power, but it will do at a pinch.

Religious symbols: Some people believe that vampires are creatures of the devil, because some vampires experience physical pain when they come in contact with crosses and holy water. If a cross or other religious object touches a vampire, the vampire could catch fire or turn into a pile of dust. Wearing a cross, Star of David or other religious item on the body will keep some vampires at bay. (Other vampires, however, aren't affected by the symbols, so be very careful not to rely on this method alone.)

GARLIC: IT'S NOT JUST FOR VAMPIRE HUNTERS ANY MORE

Part of the lily family, Liliaceae, and classified as *Allium sativum*, common garlic has been grown for centuries for use both in cooking and in medical remedies. It grows with small, off-white, six-petal flowers. Most supermarkets will sell you a 'bulb' (a large grouping, also called a head, of individual cloves), and each bulb provides anywhere from fifteen to twenty cloves.

It's also very easy to grow a garlic plant, and as an added bonus, the flowers are pretty. Go to a nursery or garden centre to find out how to grow some.

THINK SMART! SIMPLY PLACING SOME HANDY VAMPIRE REPELLENT

AROUND YOUR ROOM CAN PREVENT THIS FROM HAPPENING TO YOU!

Stakes: Driving a wooden stake (a large stick with a sharply pointed end) through the heart of a vampire is one of the best ways to kill it. If a vampire even sees a person carrying a stake, it may realize what's going on and head in the opposite direction. The best wooden stakes are made of hardwood, such as pine or ash. (Helpful hint: Most wooden baseball bats are made of ash.)

Axes: Decapitating, or beheading, a vampire is the second-best way to kill one. Once a vampire's body is running around on its own, the head isn't in control and neither part will be able to feed. Axes, usually found in woodsheds, are the best tools to use for this job.

Fire: Vampires can catch fire very easily – just one spark will do the trick. That's because for all their life-like qualities, vampires' bodies are dry and brittle. Vampires will always keep far away from lit candles or campfires.

Seeds, grains, knotted string: According to some accounts, vampires have a very odd fascination with seeds, grains and knotted string. Apparently, any time they're around small seeds and grain, they feel the need to *count* every single kernel. No one can figure out why, but it's considered an excellent way to keep them distracted. In the same way, when vampires come anywhere near a piece of tangled string, they cannot resist the impulse to untie every knot. Tossing a handful of rice or a very tangled ball of twine could keep a vampire occupied for a *long* time.

1. Get two sticks, one approximately twice the length of the other. Wooden chopsticks from a Chinese restaurant are perfect for this job – just break one of them in half.

2. Arrange the two sticks into a cross and join them where they overlap. A twisty-tie that comes with a plastic food bag will do the trick. Wrap it around in a figure-of-eight pattern oriented straight up and down, then around again with the 'eight' lying on its side.

3. Wrap the twisty-tie around, until the pieces are secure. You may need more than one twisty tie.

4. Hold the cross by the long part, and keep it up and in the vampire's line of sight for maximum power.

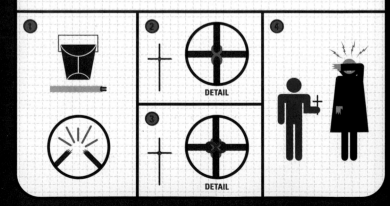

Here is a great knot that is very difficult to undo. But if time is limited, a simple 'overhead' (or shoelace) knot is enough to distract a vampire. When tied with thin string, this knot is difficult to untie.

SQUARE KNOT

There's a little saying that most people use to remember this knot: 'Right over left, left over right.' Tie two ordinary knots, but pay attention to which way you tie them. The first knot should have the string in your right hand, going over and around the left-hand string. The second knot must be the reverse, where you take the piece now in your left hand and wrap it over and around the right-hand piece.

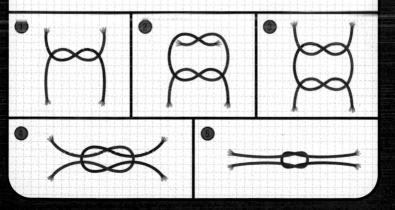

TORCH

WOODEN STAKE

NOTEBOOK

WATCH

RELIGIOUS SYMBOLS

GARLIC

SNACKS

CHAPTER THREE

THE VAMPIRE HUNTER'S FIELD GUIDE

Because of the dangers involved, it's always best to hunt
for vampires in a group. There are no right or wrong ways
to hunt down these powerful beings, but success usually
comes in larger groups.

Before you start looking for vampires, it's important to
have (1) the proper equipment for a vampire hunt, (2)

information on where to find a vampire and (3) a game plan for tracking any vampires you do find.

WHAT YOU'LL NEED

Here is a checklist of the essential tools that no Vampire Hunter should be without.

- **Pen or pencil:** For good note-taking, naturally.
- **Vampire Hunter's Notebook:** (see pp. 84–5) For note-taking.
- **Torch:** Vampires can see in the dark very easily, but people can't. Be prepared.
- **Watch:** Just in case others sight a vampire on the same night, it's helpful to compare sighting times to determine if it was the same vampire or not.
- **Good trainers:** Always be ready to run away!
- **Snacks:** You may end up waiting for a long time.

- **Garlic:** One of the most effective tools for repelling a vampire.
- **Cross:** This will also repel a vampire. In an emergency, a person could also burn a vampire by touching it with the cross.
- **Wooden stake:** This sends a clear message to the vampire and will put it on the defensive.

WHERE TO FIND A VAMPIRE

No one can say for sure where vampires are most likely to be found. Although their legend originated in Eastern Europe, over the years they've done a lot of travelling, and today there are reports of vampire sightings all over the world.

Many Vampire Hunters worry that their home towns are too 'ordinary'—but these are just the kinds of places

BE AN INTERNATIONAL VAMPIRE HUNTER! LEARN THE NAMES OF VAMPIRES IN OTHER COUNTRIES.

1. AFRICA
   obayifo (oh-buy-ee-foe)
2. BOSNIA
   lampir (laump-ear)
3. BULGARIA
   obur (oh-burr)
4. CHINA
   jiang-shi (jiang-shur)
5. FRANCE
   mélusine (meh-loo-seen)
6. GERMANY
   nachtzehrer
   (knocked-zeh-rur)
7. GREECE
   vrykilakas
   (vree-kee-lah-kas)
8. INDIA
   kali (kah-lee)
9. ITALY
   vampiri (vam-pee-ree)
10. JAPAN
    kappa (kahp-ah)
11. PHILIPPINES
    aswang (ah-swang)
12. ROMANIA
    strigoi (stree-goy)
13. RUSSIA
    uppyr (oop-ir)

Russia **13**

Kazakhstan

Uzbekistan

rbaijan Turkmenistan Tajikistan
enia

Iran Afghanistan

Pakistan

t

Qatar

U.A.E.

Oman

emen

uti

omalia

Mongolia

Kyrgyzsta

China **4**

N. Korea **10**

S. Korea

India **8**

Nepal

Bhutan

Bangladesh

Myanmar
(Burma)

Laos

Taiwan

*North
Pacific
Ocean*

Thailand

Vietnam

Cambodia **11**

Andaman
Islands
(India)

Sri
Lanka

Brunei

Malaysia

Singapore

Indonesia

*Indian
Ocean*

ique

Madagascar

Mauritius

Australia

vampires like to haunt. The following tips will help make a search more productive.

① **Look close to home.**

Because of their close link to their native soil, most vampires stay near their home towns to find fresh blood. Vampires are loyal creatures and will generally stay in their home town or continually return to it.

② **Check out the local cemetery.**

Within a particular city, vampires are most likely to be seen in the very graveyard where they were buried. Because they have to rest regularly in their coffins, young vampires in particular will return to their coffins daily.

③ **Look for clues outside the cemetery.**

When they're not resting in their graves, most vampires are usually out hunting. In their first few months, new vampires have been known to attack their family and friends.

Keep an eye out for multiple deaths within a short amount of time in one family, then find out where the first relative to die was buried. This individual may be the active vampire. (It is possible to surprise the vampire on its way back home after a night of feeding.)

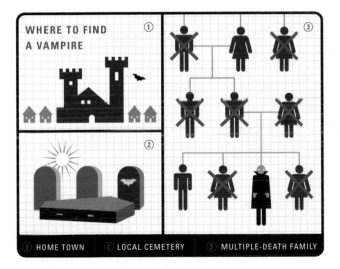

WHERE TO FIND A VAMPIRE

① HOME TOWN   ② LOCAL CEMETERY   ③ MULTIPLE-DEATH FAMILY

VAMPIRES SOMETIMES CARRY VICTIMS BACK TO THEIR LAIR.

1. TRANSYLVANIA

Transylvania is not explored very often
by tourists, but, as the home of the
bloody Count Dracula, it has the world's
richest vampire history. Bram Stoker
set his novel <u>Dracula</u> here, and today
in Transylvania visitors can see castles
just like the one the count lived in.

2. HIGHGATE CEMETERY

Located on Swain's Lane in north London,
Highgate Cemetery is famed as the burial
site of Lucy (the inspiration for another
character in Bram Stoker's <u>Dracula</u>).

In the late 1960s, dozens of foxes
were found dead in the cemetery, and several
young women fell ill after walking among
the graves. Hundreds of Vampire Hunters
descended on the cemetery, and things have
been quiet in Highgate ever since. But
anything can happen....

3. LAFAYETTE CEMETERY

Located in the 1400 block of Washington Avenue (Garden District) of New Orleans, Lafayette Cemetery is famed as America's best spot for vampire sightings. Take a look at all the above-ground crypts: the graves are very different from most others in the nation, which are usually underground. (That's because New Orleans is below sea level—in the event of a flood, bodies buried in the ground would simply rise to the surface.)

With above-ground tombs, vampires can come and go much more easily, without having to crawl through dirt to reach the surface.

Near the cemetery is the house of Anne Rice, author of <u>The Vampire Chronicles</u>.

HOW TO TRACK A VAMPIRE

① **Do not go alone.**

It is much better to work with other people you trust, since one person is simply no match for a vampire.

Some of the most successful vampire tracking parties, like the ones that went to Highgate Cemetery in the 1960s, were composed of nearly a hundred people! Think about it – the more hunters there are in a group, the more likely they are to find and conquer a vampire. As the saying goes, there's safety in numbers.

② **Be prepared.**

Make sure every person is armed with the right objects to repel vampires, as listed in the checklist of essential tools (see pages 44–5).

③ **Do your research.**

Remember that vampires look just like anyone else –

large crowds won't deter them, as they will easily blend in. The keys are to try to predict the vampire's next move and to wait. Remember the warning signs from the previous chapter:

Look for suspicious behaviour.

- Are there people in your town who haven't appeared to age in several years?
- Can older people in your neighbourhood remember a time when your suspect looked younger? If not, that person may be living in the frozen time of a vampire.

Look for vampiric characteristics.

- Review the list of common vampire characteristics.
- Is the person you suspect considered a 'night person' – most active when the sun is down?
- Does the suspect exhibit moodiness, a quick temper, or other unpredictable behaviour?

WHERE TO LOOK FOR VAMPIRES

- Blood banks
- Hospitals
- Alaska in November, December and January, when the days are dark nearly 24 hours
- Windowless basements
- Bat houses in zoos
- Nail salons (to keep those claws trimmed and neat)
- Sunglasses shops

WHERE *NOT* TO LOOK FOR VAMPIRES

- Gilroy, California (garlic capital of the world)
- Alaska in June, July and August, when there are nearly 24 hours of sunlight per day
- Tanning salons
- Wool shops (too many tangled balls of string)
- Italian restaurants (all that garlic)
- Chinese restaurants (all that rice)
- Religious events

Try the garlic test.

- Invite the vampire to a dinner party. Prepare lots of spaghetti and several loaves of garlic bread, and watch for reactions. Maybe you can even ask the suspected vampire to help chop garlic – does he or she refuse to get near the stuff?

④ **Mobilize your team early in the morning.**

Go to the cemetery you think houses a vampire. Check to see if the earth around any graves has been disturbed. Settle in and wait for sunrise. If you see any suspicious people entering the cemetery very early in the morning, you may be on the trail of a genuine vampire.

⑤ **Record and track the movements of the suspected vampire in your Hunter's Notebook (pages 84–5).**

- What time does the vampire return in the morning?

- What time does the vampire leave at night?

- Does it always travel the same paths and have a routine?
- Are there sick people along the vampire's route?
- Does it avoid areas with churches?

THE DRACULA MUSEUM

This museum is the place to go for anyone looking to learn more about vampires in general and Dracula in particular. Located in New York City, USA, the Dracula Museum houses some of the best artefacts and objects related to vampires from all over the world.

Unfortunately, it's open by appointment to members only. Members of the Count Dracula Fan Club are automatically given membership to the museum. Contact Dr. Youngson, the museum's curator, for more information:

COUNT DRACULA FAN CLUB
Penthouse N · 29 Washington Square West
New York, NY 10011 USA

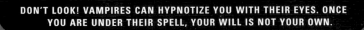
DON'T LOOK! VAMPIRES CAN HYPNOTIZE YOU WITH THEIR EYES. ONCE YOU ARE UNDER THEIR SPELL, YOUR WILL IS NOT YOUR OWN.

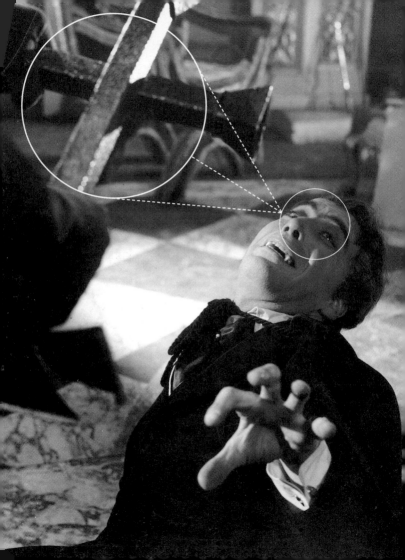

CHAPTER FOUR

WHAT TO DO WHEN YOU FIND A VAMPIRE

Anyone who comes face to face with a vampire is automatically in great danger. The immediate goal is to evade the creature and avoid its powers. Then, a good Vampire Hunter will focus on the proper steps for defeating it – and making sure it never returns.

THE FIRST RULES OF DEFENCE

① Never invite a vampire inside your house.

If a vampire is on the loose, the first and most important rule is never to invite a suspected vampire into the house. Once a vampire is invited indoors, it becomes indestructible. None of the methods listed above will work. (It is possible to *retract* an invitation, but only before the vampire has set foot in the house.)

Note: Vampires that enter a house *uninvited* are still vulnerable to any repellents placed near them.

② Search during the day, and stay outside or in well-lit areas if possible.

Because vampires are weakened or even killed by sunlight, the outdoors is the safest place to be, especially on sunny days. A vampire will not come near people exposed to direct sunlight, because the sunlight would render the vampire powerless.

Daylight is also the best time to proceed with research (obituary reading, gravestone research), in preparation for finding the vampire in person.

③ **Keep the vampire busy.**

Talk to it. Tell it jokes, read it a story, distract it. Just keep talking – don't let it interrupt. Even when a vampire is hungry, it is always a sucker for a good story – isn't everybody? Or rely on the time-honoured tricks described in the repellent section: drop seeds or knotted string near the vampire.

ALTHOUGH THE STEREOTYPICAL VAMPIRE IS MALE, FEMALE VAMPIR

RE ON THE RISE AND JUST AS DEADLY!

HOW TO COMMUNICATE WITH A VAMPIRE

It is best not to get into a conversation with vampires, because their powers are subtle yet extraordinarily potent. But if you must, follow these steps to avoid falling under a vampire's spell:

① **Avoid eye contact as much as possible.**

Remember, vampires' eyes are hypnotic, and they will not hesitate to use them to gain control over you.

② **Keep a good distance.**

No person should stand within an arm's length of any vampire! With their superhuman strength, vampires can quickly grab a person and bite them.

③ **Don't worry about the language barrier.**

Though vampires come from many different countries, most people will meet vampires in their own home towns, and vampires can usually communicate in English without a problem. (The problem is deciding what to say!)

④ **Keep talking.**

An excellent tactic is to keep talking to the vampire, especially if the encounter takes place just before dawn. If the vampire is distracted, it may not realize that daybreak is only minutes away. Once the sun is up, a Vampire Hunter can make a quick escape – or take measures to destroy the now-vulnerable vampire. (See 'How to Destroy a Vampire', pages 70–1)

These are all good methods for keeping the vampire at bay, but inevitably stronger measures are needed to fend off a vampire attack.

HOW TO DESTROY A VAMPIRE

When it's time to deal with the vampire directly, use any of these essential tactics to defeat it. These methods are ranked in order of priority and effectiveness.

Keep the law in mind at all times: a person must be under attack to be able to claim self-defence. Besides, it would be silly to provoke a vampire into doing something rash, wouldn't it?

1) **Stake the vampire.**

Grasp the stake firmly by its thickest part. The goal is to push the stake directly through the heart – no other part will do.

Sneak up behind the vampire if possible. Take it by surprise, and once it's facing you, throw your body weight into the thrust and stake the vampire in the middle of the chest. It's important to plunge the stake in with one blow, because stabbing the vampire twice will bring it back to 'life' and make it invincible. Once it is staked, get out of reach as soon as possible, because a vampire is going to be *angry* until it dies.

② **Set the vampire on fire.**

Try setting things around the vampire on fire – eventually a spark or flame will lick the vampire or its clothing and set it ablaze. Matches, candles and small campfires will do the trick. Crosses or other holy images will burn the vampire, so try hitting it with these as well.

SLAYER (slā′ er) noun. a person born once every generation with the amazing strength and skill to hunt vampires where they gather – and destroy them.

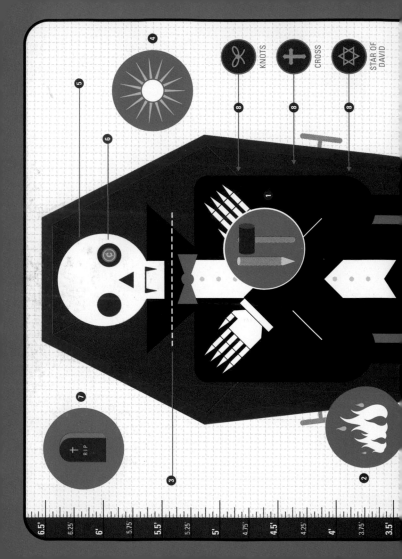

KNOTS

CROSS

STAR OF
DAVID

RIP

6.5'
6.25'
6'
5.75'
5.5'
5.25'
5'
4.75'
4.5'
4.25'
4'
3.75'
3.5'

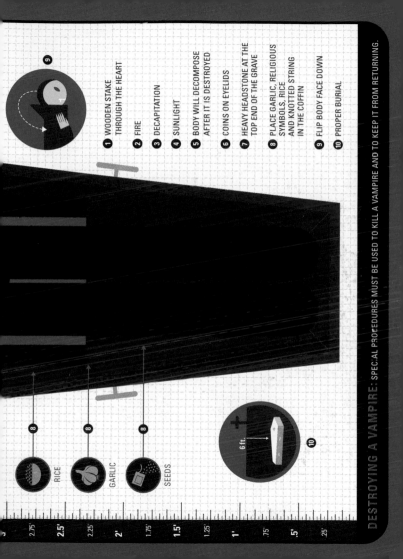

1. WOODEN STAKE THROUGH THE HEART
2. FIRE
3. DECAPITATION
4. SUNLIGHT
5. BODY WILL DECOMPOSE AFTER IT IS DESTROYED
6. COINS ON EYELIDS
7. HEAVY HEADSTONE AT THE TOP END OF THE GRAVE
8. PLACE GARLIC, RELIGIOUS SYMBOLS, RICE AND KNOTTED STRING IN THE COFFIN
9. FLIP BODY FACE DOWN
10. PROPER BURIAL

RICE

GARLIC

SEEDS

6 ft.

DESTROYING A VAMPIRE: SPECIAL PROCEDURES MUST BE USED TO KILL A VAMPIRE AND TO KEEP IT FROM RETURNING.

③ **Decapitate the vampire.**

If an axe or another sharp tool is handy, come at the vampire swinging. One powerful swipe of the blade across the neck should do the trick. Watch out for the body, though, because it will continue to run around for some time after it's beheaded.

Some experts will even recommend decapitating vampires that have already been staked or set on fire, just to make sure the vampires are really dead.

The body and the head should be buried separately.

④ **Force the vampire into the sun.**

There is always the chance that a vampire will disintegrate upon contact with a ray of sunlight. Tricking the vampire into staying out past dawn or even forcing it outside during the day could turn the vampire into a pile of dust in a second.

74

HOW TO PREVENT VAMPIRES FROM MULTIPLYING

Now that you're prepared to hunt and defend yourself against a vampire, you can see just how powerful these beings are – and how difficult they are to destroy.

That's why experts say that absolutely the best way to combat a vampire is never to allow it to come into existence in the first place. Here are some sure-fire tips for preventing a corpse from becoming a vampire.

Coins: This method is of uncertain origin, passed down through generations, but it's been known to work. Placing coins on the corpse's eyelids helps it pay its way into the world of the dead. According to this tradition, if corpses do not have money with them, they will be refused entry and will return to the world of mortals, destined to stay there for ever.

(No one's quite sure how much it costs to get in, so use coins with high value. Better to have too much than not enough.)

Headstone: Get a very heavy, very large headstone (granite is good) and place it at the top end of the grave. Traditionally, headstones were used to keep a vampire from sitting up – it would knock itself out on the hard stone!

Garlic: Place a clove or two of garlic in the corpse's mouth. (Placing it around the body is thought to work too.)

Religious symbols, seeds and knots: Place many crosses, Stars of David, cups of rice and knotted string in the coffin.

Flipping the body: Bury the body face down in the coffin. If the corpse becomes a vampire, its urge to climb out will only result in digging itself the wrong way – deeper into the ground.

Proper burial: Make sure the body is buried properly, six feet deep underground. Without six feet of heavy dirt over the body, it could become active much more quickly.

Staking: Plunge a stake into the corpse while it is in the coffin. Alternatively, a stake could be placed in the ground above the coffin, which would cause a vampire to impale itself when it climbs out of the grave.

Decapitation: Decapitate the corpse, and then bury the head and body separately.

① VAMPIRE ATTACKING ② VICTIM

③ ④ ⑤ ⑥ WITNESSES

REPORTING THE INCIDENT

Now that you've successfully discovered a vampire, or maybe even killed one off, it's time for a congratulatory pause. But wait—you *did* remember to report the incident to the proper authorities, didn't you? Your local police station must be aware of all vampire sightings and other threats to your community.

Now that you've reported your findings (which were all carefully recorded in your Hunter's Notebook), it's *really* time for that congratulatory pause. But you shouldn't relax for long, because there's always the chance that there are more vampires in your town.

Even if you haven't yet located a vampire, don't despair. You're equipped with all the best information there is for tracking, finding and conquering one.

Keep your eyes open (especially at night!) for any strange activity. You never know, there might just be an undead neighbour roaming the streets, looking for fresh blood.

① VAMPIRIC STRANGER LURKING THE STREETS │ ② *YOUR* NEIGHBOURHOOD?

③ TOWN CENTRE | ④ SPOOKY OLD CASTLE UP ON A HILL

APPENDIX: FURTHER READING AND VIEWING

BOOKS

Read all about it! There are hundreds of books about vampires. Here are some of the best in vampire fiction:

Buffy the Vampire Slayer (series, young adult), by Richie Tankersley Cusick (No. 1: 1997)

Dracula, by Bram Stoker (1897)

I, Vampire, by Michael Romkey (1990)

The Last Vampire (series, young adult), by Christopher Pike (No. 1: 1994)

The Vampire Chronicles, by Anne Rice: *Interview with the Vampire* (1976), *The Vampire Lestat* (1985), *The Queen of the Damned* (1988), *The Tale of the Body Thief* (1992)

Vampire Hunter, by Michael Romkey (1999)

The Vampire Papers, by Michael Romkey (1994)

The Vampire Princess, by Michael Romkey (1996)

The Vampire Virus, by Michael Romkey (1998)

Even though vampires don't show up on normal film, there have been many films and TV programmes made about vampires (these feature actors, who do show up on film).

FILMS

Bram Stoker's Dracula, directed by Francis Ford Coppola (1992)

Buffy the Vampire Slayer, directed by Fran Rubel Kuzui (1992)

Dracula, directed by Tod Browning, and starring
  Bela Lugosi (1931)

The Horror of Dracula, directed by Terence Fisher, and starring
  Christopher Lee (1958)

The Lost Boys, directed by Joel Schumacher (1987)

Nosferatu, directed by F. W. Murnau (1922)

Once Bitten, directed by Howard Storm (1985)

TELEVISION

Angel, airs on Channel 4

Buffy the Vampire Slayer, airs on BBC 2

VAMPIRE HUNTER'S NOTEBOOK

SIGHTING DATE:

SIGHTING TIME:

LOCATION:

VAMPIRE APPEARANCE:

HEIGHT:

WEIGHT:

HAIR COLOUR:

SKIN COLOUR:

TEETH:

EYES:

REFLECTION (YES/NO):

WEAPONS USED (CHECK ALL THAT APPLY):

- ◯ CROSS
- ◯ SUNLIGHT
- ◯ HOLY WATER
- ◯ KNOTS
- ◯ SEEDS
- ◯ WOODEN STAKE

COMMENTS:

VAMPIRE HUNTER IDENTIFICATION

"NONMORTUOS QUAESIVI"
"I have sought the Undead"

The bearer of this ID has read and understood *The Vampire Hunter's Handbook*. Ownership of this ID certifies that the bearer is well-versed in vampire analysis, investigation, and extermination. The bearer should also be granted unrestricted access to castles, crypts, tombs, cemeteries, basements, root cellars, mortuaries, blood banks, and the entire region of Transylvania.